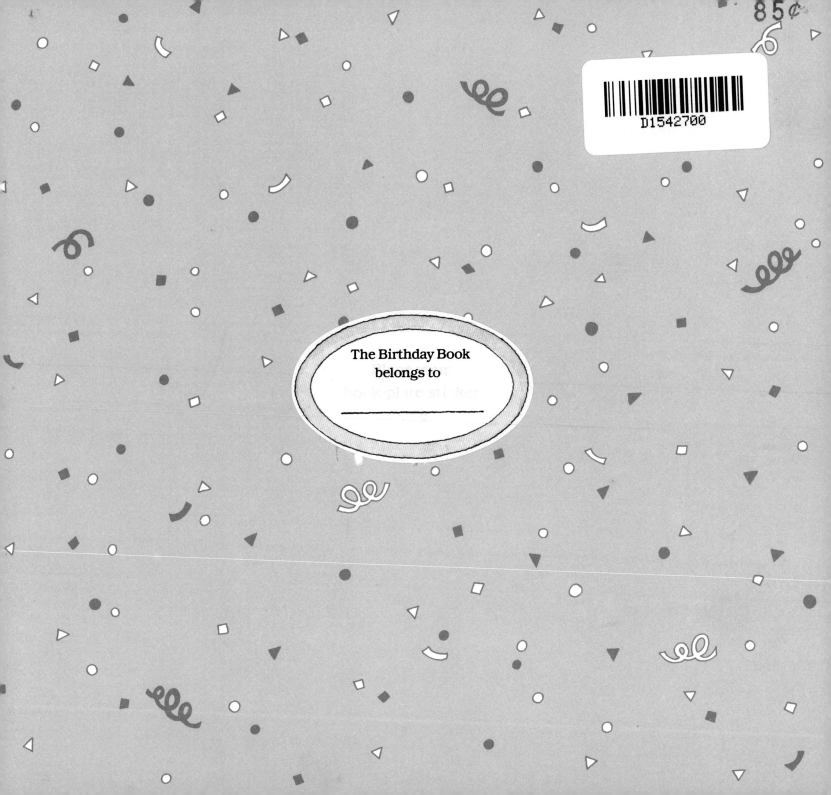

The Birthday Book
belongs to

_____

85¢

D1542700

THE BIRTHDAY BOOK

THE BIRTHDAY BOOK

Stickers to Stick & Cards to Create
for Every Month of the Year

DEBI PERNA

Greey de Pencier Books

Books from OWL are published by Greey de Pencier Books,
56 The Esplanade, Suite 302, Toronto, Ontario M5E 1A7

*The Owl colophon is a trademark of the Young Naturalist Foundation.
Greey de Pencier Books is a licensed user of the trademarks of the
Young Naturalist Foundation.

This book was published with the generous support of the Canada Council
and the Ontario Arts Council.

Canadian Cataloguing in Publication Data

Perna, Debi
The Birthday Book

ISBN 0-920775-57-8

1. Birthday books — Juvenile literature. 2. Birthdays — Calendars —
Juvenile literature.
3. Seasons — Juvenile literature. 4. Amusements — Juvenile literature.
I. Title

GT2430.P47 1991   j394.2   C90-095306-3

Design: Debi Perna
Design Consultant: Wycliffe Smith

Printed in Hong Kong
A   B   C   D   E   F

INTRODUCTION

What is your favourite day of the year? Is it your birthday? In this book you can find lots of birthday celebrations and watch the seasons change as we follow five friends through the twelve months of the year. Each month has a space for you to record special birthdays, and instructions for making a super birthday card. You'll find more about birthdays and the months of the year at the back of the book, along with dozens of stickers to fill in and stick in *The Birthday Book*.

When is your birthday? Write the date on your own special birthday sticker and stick it in the space for stickers under the month of your birthday. Write the names and birthdays of all your family and friends on other stickers and stick them under their birthday months. *The Birthday Book* will help you remember these special birthdays year after year.

Do you like birthday cards? A nice way to wish someone happy birthday is to give a home-made card. You can make your very own cards by following the card instructions for each month of the year. Be sure to take care when using any cutting tools. (You may need just a little help from an adult.) Your family and friends will love receiving these special home-made cards.

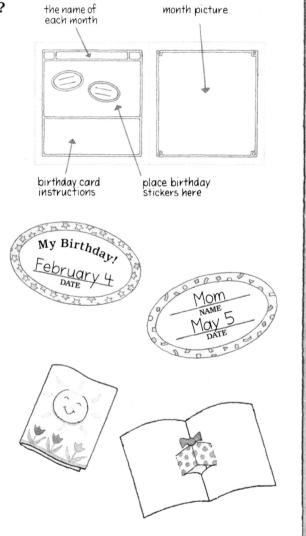

the name of each month

month picture

birthday card instructions

place birthday stickers here

My Birthday!
February 4
DATE

Mom
NAME
May 5
DATE

JANUARY

BIRTHDAY STICKERS

Folding Card

Fold a piece of paper in half.
Fold the top section in half again.
Draw a picture on the front across
the fold. Open the card and
finish the picture on the inside.

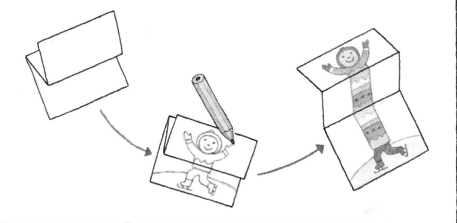

B I R T H D A Y   S T I C K E R S

Window Card

Draw a square on the front of the
card. Open the card and cut out
the square. Close the card and
draw a picture in the window.
Finish the picture on the inside.

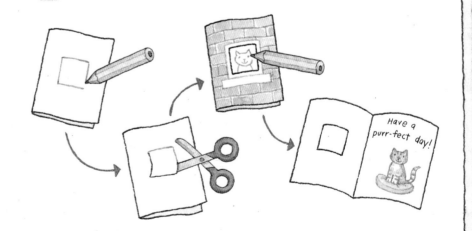

Have a purr-fect day!

MARCH

B I R T H D A Y   S T I C K E R S

Cut-Out Card

Draw a picture on the front of the
card so that part of the picture
runs off the folded edge. Cut
around the outline of the picture,
except for the folded side.
Decorate the card.

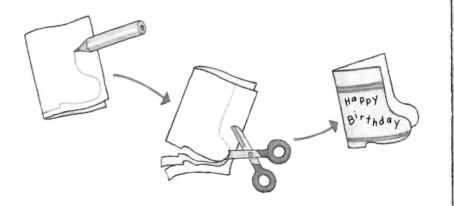

APRIL

Dot-to-Dot Card

Draw a simple picture in light pencil. With a marker, place dots along the pencil lines and draw in parts of the picture. Number the dots in order and erase the pencil lines.

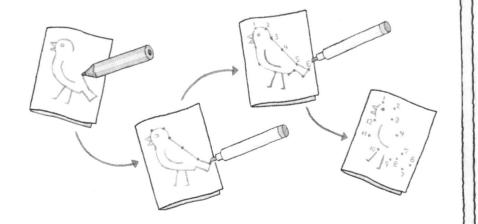

MAY

B I R T H D A Y   S T I C K E R S

Kite Card

Cut a small square from a piece of paper. Fold each corner into the centre. Stick the square to the front of the card. Print a message inside the square and decorate the card.

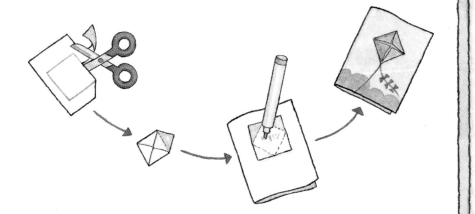

JUNE

B I R T H D A Y   S T I C K E R S

Open Flower Card

Draw a short line down the middle of the card. Draw half of a flower on one side. Cut out the flower except along the line and fold it back. Colour the flower and finish the picture.

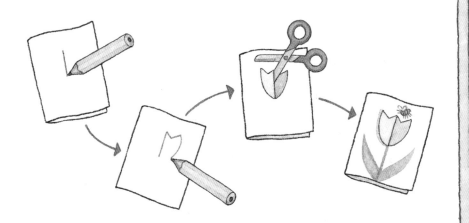

JULY

B I R T H D A Y   S T I C K E R S

Sun Card

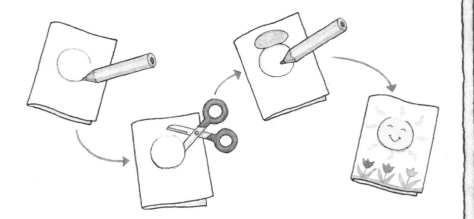

Draw a circle on the front of the card. Cut out the circle leaving the top section attached. Fold back the cut-out circle and print a message inside. Close the flap and decorate the card.

AUGUST

B I R T H D A Y   S T I C K E R S

Pop-Up Card

Cut two lines into the folded edge
of the card. Fold the cut strip
back, then forward, and push it
through to the inside. Stick a
blank card to the outside of your
pop-up card and decorate.

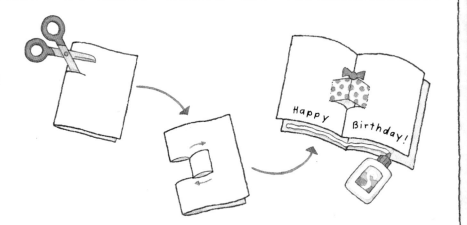

SEPTEMBER

B I R T H D A Y   S T I C K E R S

Pull-Tab Card

Open the card and cut two slots
on the inside. Cut a narrow strip
of paper for a pull tab. Insert it
through the bottom slot and back
through the top slot. Decorate
your pull-tab card.

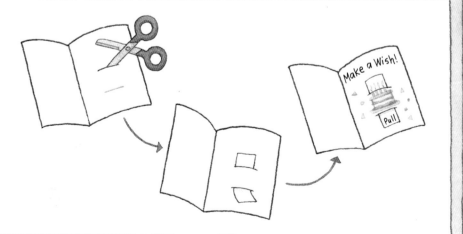

B I R T H D A Y   S T I C K E R S

Mask Card

Draw a small circle on the front of the card, about 2.5 cm from the folded edge. Cut out the circle through both layers of paper. Open the card and draw a face to make a mask.

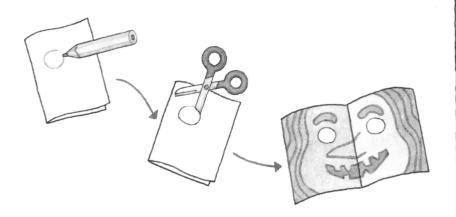

NOVEMBER

B I R T H D A Y   S T I C K E R S

Potato Stamp Card

Have an adult cut a small potato
in half and carve the flat side
into a shape. Dip the potato shape
into a flat dish of paint. Press
the potato stamp onto the card
to make a pretty pattern.

DECEMBER

B I R T H D A Y   S T I C K E R S

Turning Circle Card

Cut a circle out of paper. Attach it to the card with a brass paper fastener. Draw a face on the circle and decorate the card. Turn the circle for a funny picture.

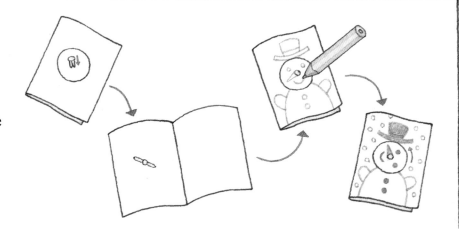

- In which month did you see each of these pictures? Read the clues and guess the months. Look back and find them. Did you remember all twelve months?

5 cups of cocoa

2 bathing birds

1 squirrel

1 bird feeder

3 robins

4 honey bees

3 daffodils

5 little boats

4 sunflowers

5 kittens

9 geese

20 snowballs

- Here's a skipping rhyme to help you remember all the months. Each jumper runs in when his or her birthday month is called. Then the months are repeated and they jump out on their birthday months. Have you tried it?

Apples, peaches, pears and plums
Tell me when your birthday comes!
January, February, March, April, May,
June, July, August, September,
October, November, December!

- Do you know the number of days in each month? February is the shortest month with only 28 days. An extra day is added to February every four years. This is called leap year. People who are born on February 29th are very special because they can only celebrate their real birthday every four years! Here's a familiar rhyme to help you remember the number of days in each month.

Thirty days hath September,
April, June and November
All the rest have thirty-one
Excepting February alone,
And that has twenty-eight days clear,
And twenty-nine in each leap year.

1 2 3 4 5
6 7 8 9 10 11
12 13 14 15 16
17 18 19 20
21 22 23
24 25 26 27
28 29 30 31

- Did you know that you have a birth stone and a birth flower? Each month of the year has its own birth symbols which are said to bring good luck. Today we follow many old birthday beliefs like this mainly for fun. Look for your birthday month on this chart to find out your birth symbols.

Month	Birth Flower	Birth Stone
January	Carnation	Garnet
February	Violet	Amethyst
March	Jonquil	Aqua-marine
April	Sweet Pea	Diamond
May	Lily-of-the-Valley	Emerald
June	Rose	Pearl
July	Larkspur	Ruby
August	Gladiolus	Sardonyx
September	Aster	Sapphire
October	Marigold	Opal
November	Chrysan-themum	Topaz
December	Holly	Turquoise

- Do you know the day of the week you were born on? Some people believe that this can tell you what sort of person you are. Find out the day of your birth, then check it in this birthday rhyme.

Monday's child is fair of face,
Tuesday's child is full of grace,
Wednesday's child is full of woe,
Thursday's child has far to go,
Friday's child is loving and giving,
Saturday's child works hard for a living,
And the child that is born on Sunday
Is handsome and happy in every way.

- Did you spot all the birthday presents and parties in this book? Look back to find them. There is one for each month! People celebrate their birthdays in many different ways. How will you celebrate your birthday this year?

HAPPY BIRTHDAY!

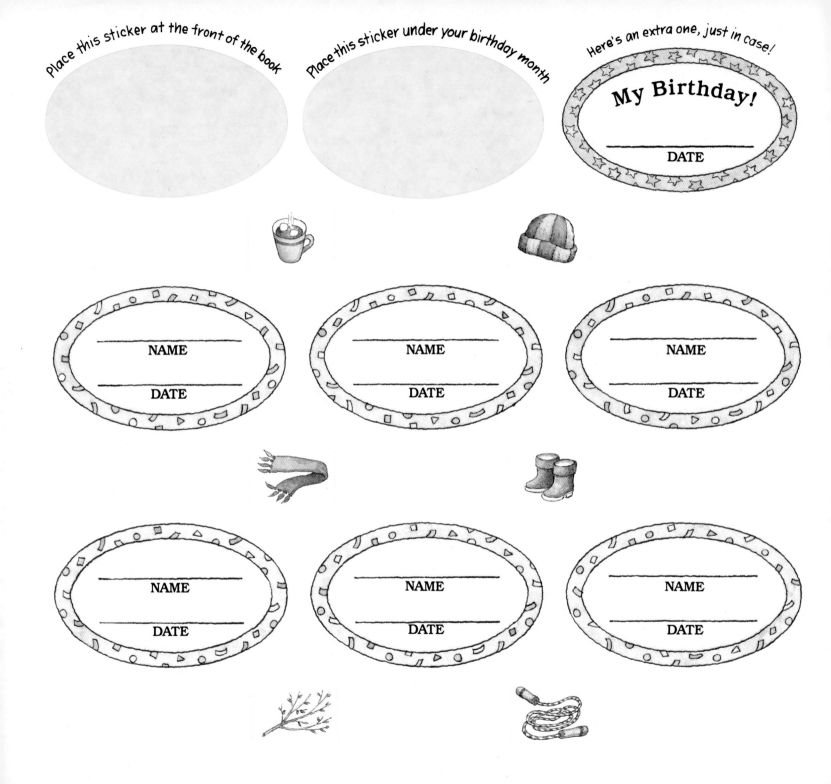

Place this sticker at the front of the book

Place this sticker under your birthday month

Here's an extra one, just in case!

My Birthday!

_____

DATE

NAME

DATE

NAME

DATE

NAME

DATE

NAME

DATE

NAME

DATE

NAME

DATE

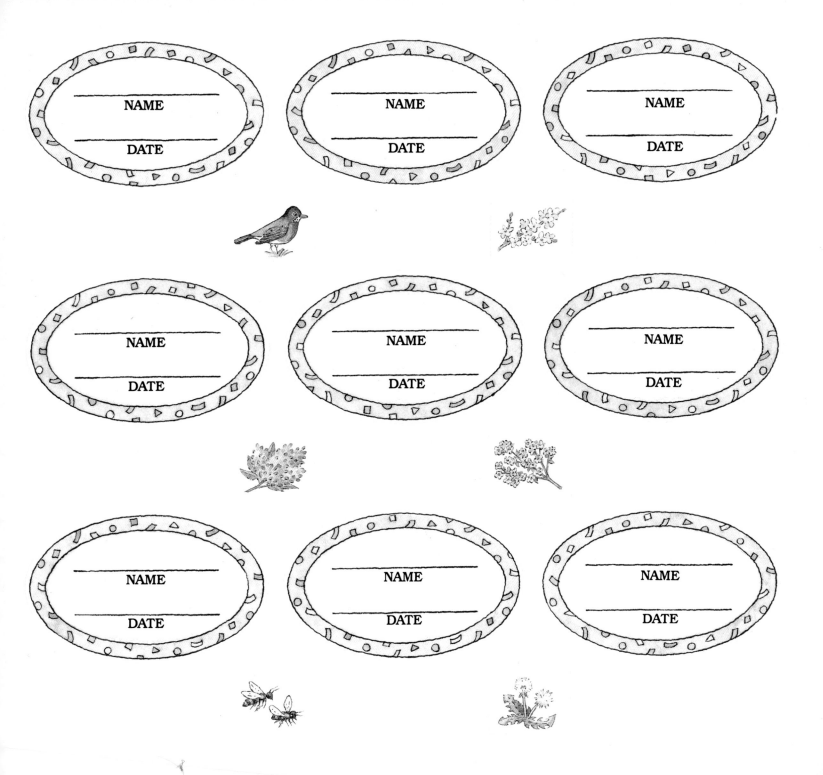

NAME

DATE

NAME

DATE

NAME

DATE

NAME

DATE

NAME

DATE

NAME

DATE

NAME

DATE

NAME

DATE

NAME

DATE

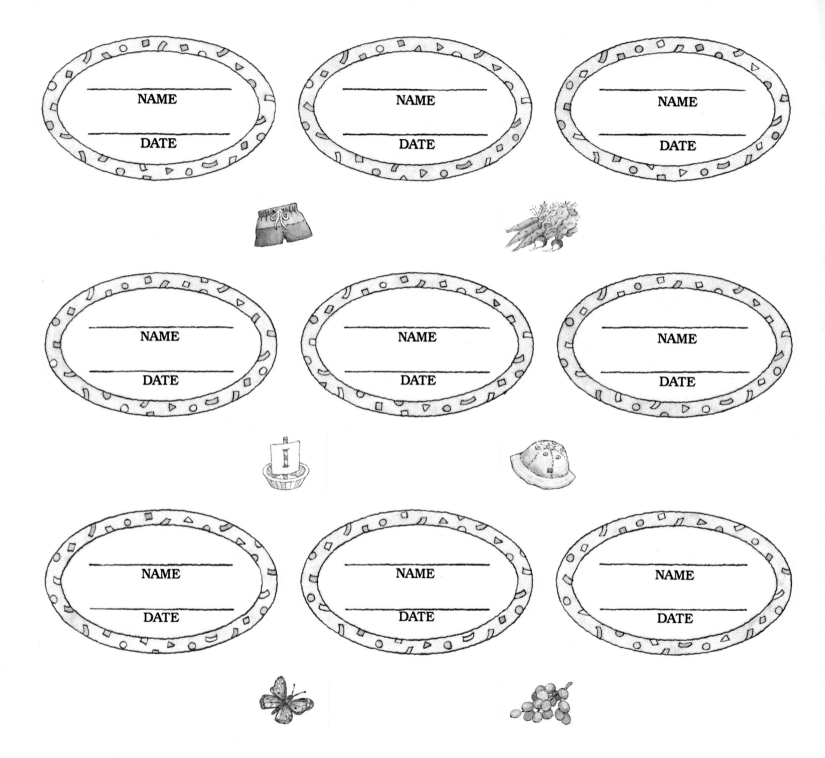

NAME

DATE

NAME

DATE

NAME

DATE

NAME

DATE

NAME

DATE

NAME

DATE

NAME

DATE

NAME

DATE

NAME

DATE

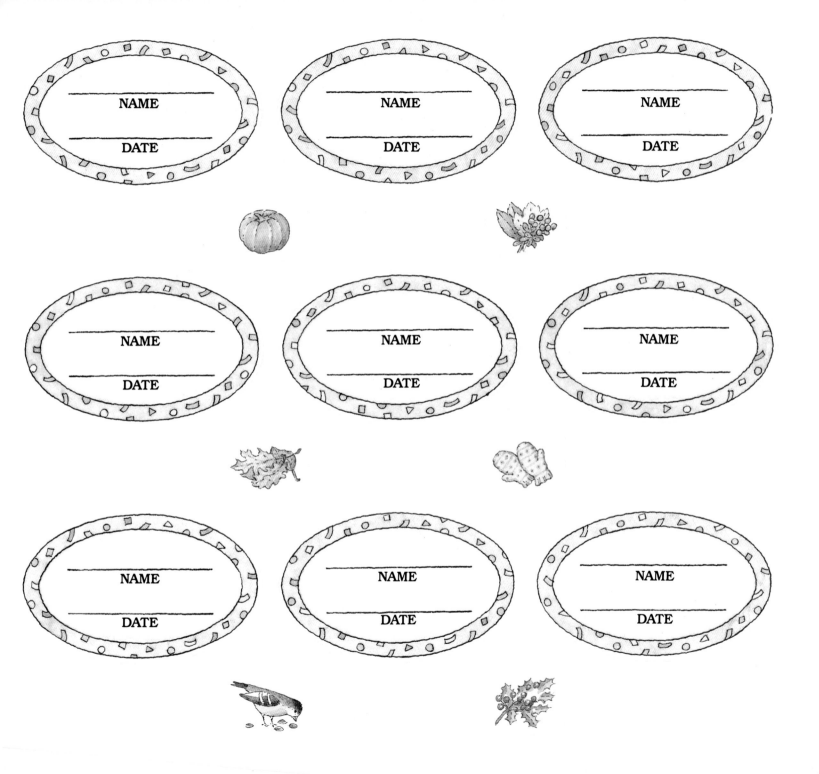

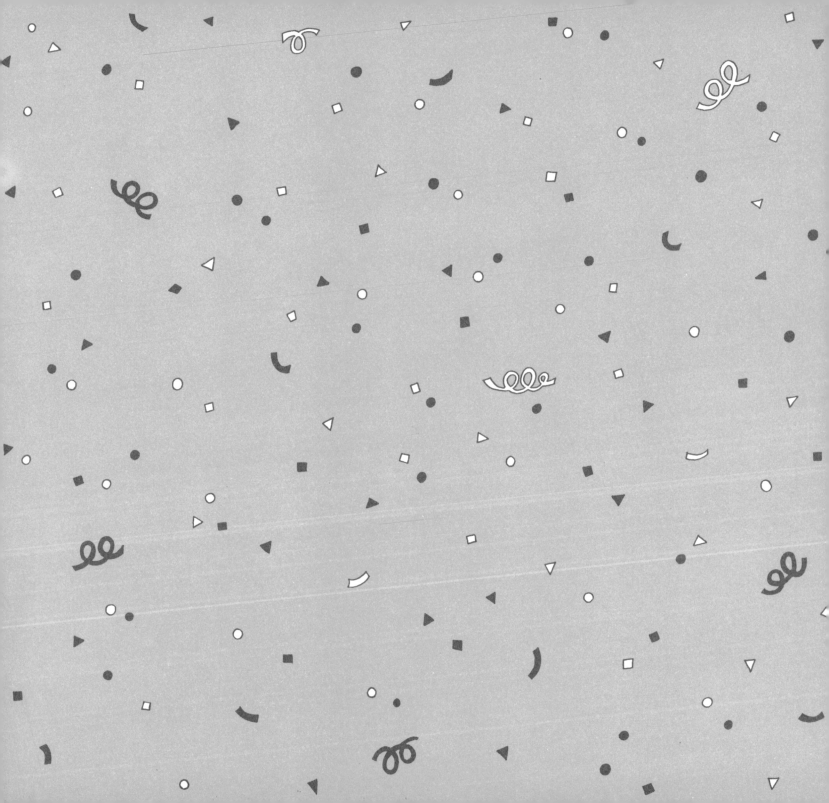